Eve Mitchell

C000146247

Clarinet
Grade 4

Pieces
for Trinity College London exams

2017-2020

Published by
Trinity College London Press
trinitycollege.com

Registered in England
Company no. 09726123

Copyright © 2016 Trinity College London Press
First impression, September 2016

Unauthorised photocopying is illegal
No part of this publication may be copied or reproduced in any
form or by any means without the prior permission of the publisher.

Printed in England by Caligraving Ltd.

Seguidilla

from *Carmen*

ed. Janet Way

Georges Bizet
(1838–1875)

Copyright © 1990 by Boosey & Hawkes Music Publishers Ltd.
Reproduced by permission from *Grade by Grade – Clarinet Grade 4* (ISMN 979-0-060-12878-3).

TRINITY
COLLEGE LONDON PRESS

Clarinet
Grade 4

Pieces
for Trinity College London exams

2017-2020

Published by
Trinity College London Press
trinitycollege.com

Registered in England
Company no. 09726123

Copyright © 2016 Trinity College London Press
First impression, September 2016

Unauthorised photocopying is illegal
No part of this publication may be copied or reproduced in any
form or by any means without the prior permission of the publisher.

Printed in England by Caligraving Ltd.

TCL 016027
ISBN 978-0-85736-555-2

Seguidilla

from *Carmen*

ed. Janet Way

Georges Bizet
(1838–1875)

Copyright © 1990 by Boosey & Hawkes Music Publishers Ltd.
Reproduced by permission from *Grade by Grade – Clarinet Grade 4* (ISMN 979-0-060-12878-3).

Après un rêve

arr. Lionel Salter

Gabriel Fauré
(1845-1924)

Arrangement Copyright © 1979 Josef Weinberger Ltd.

3

Branch Line

from *Locomotive Suite*

Colin Cowles
(born 1940)

Copyright © 1994 by Fentone Music Ltd. International Copyright secured.
All rights reserved. Reprinted by permission of Hal Leonard MGB Ltd.

Allegro con fuoco

no. 5 from *Suite in Five*

Paul Harris

Copyright © 1985 G. Ricordi & Co. (London) Ltd.

Trio
from *Quintet for Clarinet and Strings K. 581*

ed. Janet Way

Wolfgang Amadeus Mozart
(1756-1791)

Copyright © 1992 by Boosey & Hawkes Music Publishers Ltd.
Reproduced by permission from *Grade by Grade – Clarinet Grade 4* (ISMN 979-0-060-12878-3).

Rondeau

arr. Alan Richardson

Henry Purcell
(1659-1695)

Copyright © 1983 Faber Music Ltd.
Reproduced from *First Book of Clarinet Solos* by permission of the publishers.
All rights reserved.

Study

Friedrich Demnitz
(1845-1890)

Copyright © 2016 Trinity College London Press

Swing Style

no. 36 from *Clarinet Studies*

Graham Lyons
(born 1936)

Copyright © 1999 Graham Lyons

Violet Enchantment

no. 4 from *Colour Studies*

Jeffery Wilson

Copyright © 2002 Camden Music, London.
Reproduced from *Colour Studies*, CM180

4

Après un rêve

arr. Lionel Salter

Gabriel Fauré
(1845-1924)

Arrangement Copyright © 1979 Josef Weinberger Ltd.

Branch Line

from *Locomotive Suite*

Colin Cowles
(born 1940)

Copyright © 1994 by FENTONE MUSIC Ltd. International Copyright secured.
All rights reserved. Reprinted by permission of Hal Leonard MGB Ltd.

Fine

D.C. al Fine

Allegro con fuoco

no. 5 from *Suite in Five*

Paul Harris

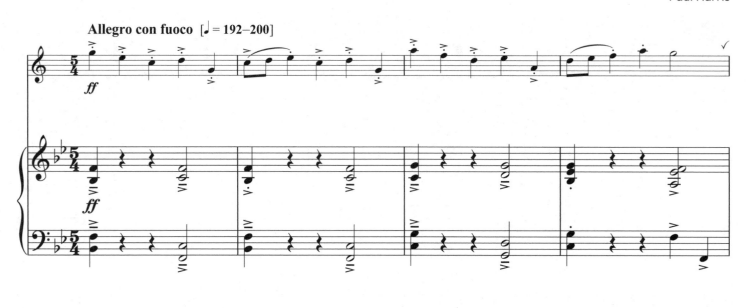

Copyright © 1985 G. Ricordi & Co. (London) Ltd.

Trio

from *Quintet for Clarinet and Strings K. 581*

ed. Janet Way

Wolfgang Amadeus Mozart
(1756-1791)

Copyright © 1992 by Boosey & Hawkes Music Publishers Ltd.
Reproduced by permission from *Grade by Grade − Clarinet Grade 4* (ISMN 979-0-060-12878-3).

Rondeau

arr. Alan Richardson

Henry Purcell
(1659-1695)

Copyright © 1983 Faber Music Ltd.
Reproduced from *First Book of Clarinet Solos* by permission of the publishers.
All rights reserved.

D.C. al Fine